SURPRISE
SURPRISE

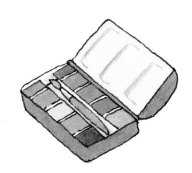

Ways to Use Surprise Surprise

This book contains carefully devised activities which help develop important early learning skills. There is no order to the activities. You can read the story first or try the questions as you read.

Words

Some questions encourage your child to discuss the story and think about the characters. You can extend the questions to talk about their own experiences. For example, what do they like to eat? What would they like for their birthday?

Maths

Some questions explore number, size, shape and colour. Try expanding these activities: How many yellow things can you find on a page?

Science

Some questions encourage observation and understanding of the natural world and technology. Try talking about experiences your child may have had too.

Time and place

Questions about the map at the end of the book invite you to work out the journey in the story and to notice how details have changed. In this way children can explore early concepts of geography and history.

Kingfisher Books, Grisewood & Dempsey Ltd
Elsley House, 24-30 Great Titchfield Street, London W1P 7AD

First published in 1994 by Kingfisher Books
2 4 6 8 10 9 7 5 3 1

Copyright © Colin and Moira Maclean 1994

Educational consultant: Jane Salt
Designed by Caroline Johnson

BRITISH LIBRARY CATALOGUING IN PUBLICATION DATA
A catalogue record for this book is available from the British Library

ISBN 1 85697 177 5

Phototypeset by Southern Positives and Negatives (SPAN),
Lingfield, Surrey
Printed and bound in Spain

KINGFISHER
Story Activity Books

SURPRISE SURPRISE

Written and illustrated by
Colin and Moira Maclean

Kingfisher Books

Amy nearly fell over it. There it was, a brown
box tied up with string, just outside her house.

A card was tied to the string. It had a picture of
red and yellow balloons and some writing but Amy
couldn't read it. Maybe it's shoes, she thought.
Then she turned it around. There was a row of little
holes along each side. Who does it belong to, she
wondered.

A woman came along, pushing a baby in a pram. Amy held up the box. "Please, do you know who this belongs to?" she asked.

The baby gurgled while his mother read the card. "It says *Happy Birthday Peter, from Mum and Dad*," she said, "but I don't know who Peter is."

It's Peter's birthday present, Amy thought. Who can Peter be? And where can I find him.

● Where are the baby's things in the picture?

● Did you have toys like this when you were a baby?

Amy decided to go and ask Mr Manzoni at the junk-yard. He knew lots of people.

"Coo-ee! Mr Manzoni!" she called.

Mr Manzoni popped out from behind an old armchair. "Oh, hello Amy," he said.

"Do you know a boy called Peter?" asked Amy.

Mr Manzoni thought hard. "That's a tricky question," he said. "Try Hadley's Café. There's a boy there and he might be Peter."

Then Mr Manzoni's dog ran up and jumped up at the box. "Wurff! Wurff!" he barked.

Mr Manzoni held his collar. "What have you got in there?" he asked. "A bone?"

- Can you see these things in Mr Manzoni's junk-yard?

- Which one belongs in a bedroom?

- Can you find all the broken things?

- What is holding up the table in the picture?

- Has a dog ever jumped up at you?

When Amy pushed open the café door, a bell tinkled. Inside a big stripey cat came up to her and patted the box with its paw. "Miaow!" it mewed. "Miaow!"

"My goodness," said Mrs Hadley. "What have you got in that box? Fish?"

"I don't think so," said Amy. "It's a birthday present for Peter."

"Oliver lives here," said Mrs Hadley. "Not Peter. Try the market garden."

- Can you see the cats in the café?

- How many bowls can you count?

- How many teapots?

- What are the people eating in the café?

- What are the cats doing?

- What would you like to eat?

It was easy to find the market garden with its great big greenhouse.

Inside, it smelled earthy and flowery.

"Look out!" said a man pushing a wheelbarrow.

Amy jumped back and nearly dropped the box. "I'm looking for Peter," she said, shyly.

"There's no Peter here," said the man. "Only Robert, and he's at his granny's. Try the greengrocer's. There might be a Peter there."

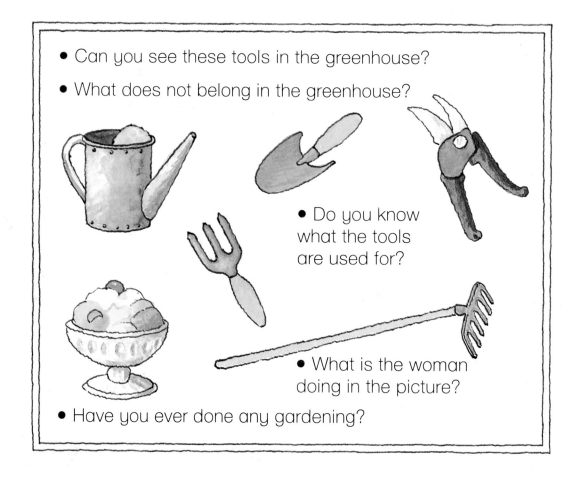

- Can you see these tools in the greenhouse?
- What does not belong in the greenhouse?
- Do you know what the tools are used for?
- What is the woman doing in the picture?
- Have you ever done any gardening?

Amy's arms were getting tired with carrying the box. At the greengrocer's she put it up on the counter beside some lettuce. "That's Peter's present," she said.

"But it's Jack who lives here," said the woman. "Peter's the postman's boy. He's…"

"Eee-eeek!" squeaked the box.

Amy jumped. "What was that?" she gasped.

The woman laughed. "I think that present is hungry," she said. "It smells lettuce."

"Oh dear," said Amy. "I *must* find Peter."

"He's at the pond in the park with Jack," the woman said. "If you're quick you'll catch them."

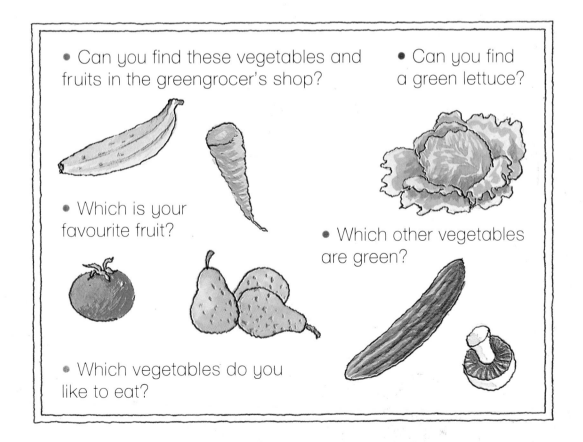

• Can you find these vegetables and fruits in the greengrocer's shop?

• Can you find a green lettuce?

• Which is your favourite fruit?

• Which other vegetables are green?

• Which vegetables do you like to eat?

- Whose hat is this?

- What has happened to it in the park?

- What else is the wind blowing? Can you see?

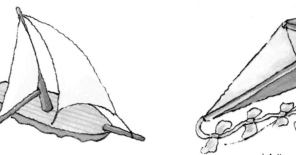

- What do you like to do in the park?

Amy ran like the wind across the park to the pond. A girl and boy were sailing boats. Another boy was fishing with a net. He had a jam jar with two little fish swimming in it.

"P-P-P," Amy puffed, "P-P-Peter..."

"Got it!" cried the boy. He plopped another wriggly fish into his jar.

"Peter!" said Amy. "Here's your present."

"I'm not Peter," said the boy. "I'm Jack. That's Peter." He pointed to the far side of the park.

Amy saw Peter go out of the park gates and raced
after him. Peter went past a statue and some men
painting a house and disappeared around the corner.
But Amy had to stop. She leaned against a lamppost,
out of breath.

"Eek-eek-eeek!" said the box.

I'll never catch up with Peter now, Amy thought,
feeling tired and miserable.

- Can you find these in the street?
  - Look at the street picture.
    - Is the ladder taller than Amy?
  - Is the dog taller than Amy?
- Which things are shorter than Amy?

At last Amy walked wearily around the corner. A postvan was standing in the front yard of a house.

A postvan! Peter's dad was the postman! Amy rang the doorbell.

"Oh! The lost present!" said Peter's mum, opening the door. "What a surprise! Come in quickly."

Peter and his dad were in the kitchen.

"Wow!" cried Peter. "My present!"

Peter's dad smiled with relief. "I thought I'd never see that present again," he said. "Let's take it into the garden."

- Can you find Peter's presents in the kitchen?

- How old is Peter today?

- Can you guess what is inside this tin?

- Which present do you think he liked best?

- What would you like for your birthday?

In the garden, Peter's mum cut the string and lifted the lid of the box. Amy held her breath. What could be inside?

"Eeeeek!" A little animal peeped out.

"It's a guinea pig," cried Peter. "Just what I wanted."

Peter and Amy fed the guinea pig while Peter's dad

went to the garden shed and fetched the
hutch he'd made for it. Then they all had
some birthday cake.

"Now I'd better drive you home," said
Peter's dad.

"Please come back tomorrow and play
with the guinea pig," said Peter's mum.

Amy and Peter and Peter's dad climbed into the front of the van and drove off. When they got to Amy's house, Amy tooted the horn to surprise her mother, the last surprise of a very surprising day.

Can you see on the map all the places where Amy went?